the OWL
and the PRAIRIE DOG

the OWL
and the PRAIRIE DOG

by berniece freschet
pictures by gilbert riswold

Charles Scribner's Sons   New York

To my sister Ada Gould

An owl, no bigger than a robin, flew through the sky.

She was full-grown now, and it was time for her to find a place of her own. So on this bright April morning Little Owl went looking for a place to live.

She was not looking for a hole in a tree, where most owls lived. This little owl was different. She was a burrowing owl. And so, she was hunting for a safe spot underground.

The little prairie owl looked very much like other owls. She had large, round, yellow eyes and a short tail. She had the same curved beak and sharp claws. And her soft, fluffy, brown feathers were marked with splotches and flecks of white.

But she did not have ear tufts, like the big owls. Instead, the feathers on her head were smooth. And although she was much smaller, she had longer legs than most owls. She also did something that none of her cousins did—whenever she met another creature, she always bowed politely.

Although she did most of her eating and playing at night, she could see very well in the daytime, and she often came out to sit on a fence post and enjoy the warm sunshine.

Little Owl hooted softly now as she came down over the wide prairie land. Below she saw a hole where a ground squirrel had once lived.

She flew down to investigate. But a short way inside the hole, she found it filled with dirt. Rain waters had clogged it with silt and gravel.

Little Owl flew on.

After a while she swooped down to a knoll. She tried to dig a hole, but the ground was too hard. She winged back into the sky.

On and on she flew.

And then, over a small hill and past a clump of sagebrush, she came to land that stretched flat in all directions. Scattered across the ground were small clumps of sagebrush and prickly cactus.

She flew lower.

A jackrabbit sat munching on a stem of red clover, his long ears alert to the slightest sound.

In an open space, beside a fallen log, two sage hens strutted and danced.

But Little Owl was looking at the many dirt mounds that dotted the land. And especially, she watched the small prairie dogs, not much bigger than squirrels, that scampered everywhere.

Some sat on top of their mounds and chattered and barked.

Some nibbled grasses.

Others pushed loose earth to the mounds, building them higher and stronger.

Little Owl had found a prairie dog town.

Underground, deep in his burrow, a prairie dog was sleeping. He lay curled up in his nest of dry grasses, his paws tucked under his chin and the black, fuzzy tip of his tail covering his nose.

The warmth and the good smell of the spring morning seeped deep into the ground. The prairie dog stirred.

His nose twitched.

He scratched an ear.

He uncurled his tail and gave it a shake.

Then he opened his dark, bright eyes and sat up in his nest. He began to tidy himself.

With the long claws on his forepaws, he combed out bits of dry leaves and grasses from his golden-tan coat. He paid special attention to his soft, furry vest, for he liked to be smooth and clean.

His long claws were most important to him. For these strong digging claws and his chisel-like teeth were the tools he worked with.

When he had finished grooming himself, he scrambled up the long, steep tunnel that led to the outside. At the top, he cautiously poked his small brown nose out of the front entrance.

Everything seemed safe. Other prairie dogs were sitting beside their doorways, and so he came out into the bright sunshine and stood on his mound.

The cloudless sky was a deep blue. The usually gray-colored sagebrush had turned a soft green and was covered with clusters of tiny yellow and white flowers. New grass pushed up through the earth. The cactus was in bloom.

A flock of blackbirds flew low while yellow-breasted meadowlarks hovered over their nests in the grasses.

The prairie dog sat up on his haunches, threw back his head, and sang. His was an odd song—part whistle, part call—filled with the happiness of a beautiful spring morning.

A short distance away, on a small rise, stood a herd of pronghorn antelopes. Suddenly alert, they lifted their handsome heads high. Then in graceful leaps and bounds, they raced away, their white rump patches gleaming in the sunlight.

Food had been hard to find during the long winter months, and the prairie dog was hungry. He scampered to a patch of green where he nibbled on the juicy stems of wild parsley.

Soon a friend joined him. The two prairie dogs stood on their hind legs and touched noses. Between nibbles, they chirruped and chattered, for prairie dogs like visiting together. After a while the friend scampered away.

Suddenly a shrill whistle interrupted the prairie dog's breakfast. It was a sentinel warning that danger was close by.

The prairie dog darted toward his mound. In one quick leap, he somersaulted down his plunge hole.

In the blue sky above, Little Owl circled the prairie dog town. She flew down and stood blinking on a sandy hummock.

In front of her, next to a tall, yellow weed, was a hole. She hopped into it.

Deep in the hole the frightened prairie dog waited, ready to defend his home. He chittered loudly.

Little Owl quickly turned to leave. She felt a tug. Someone tweaked out one of her tailfeathers! As fast as she could, she scrambled out of the tunnel.

The furious prairie dog followed. He barked angrily at Little Owl, jerking his tail defiantly with every bark.

And then it seemed as if every member of the town came out of his hole to scold her.

How noisy they were!

Little Owl bowed politely and backed away. The prairie dogs barked. She bowed again. The prairie dogs scolded louder.

The uproar frightened Little Owl. She flattened herself close to the earth. She turned her head halfway around, looking for a place to hide.

Close by Little Owl saw another hole. No angry prairie dog stood guard by this one.

There were many abandoned homes in the town, for prairie dogs often leave their old burrows to build new ones.

But still Little Owl hesitated.

A prairie dog rushed close, barking furiously. Little Owl hopped down into the hole. She waited. Nothing happened. Perhaps she would be safe here. It was cool, and dark, and best of all, the noise seemed far away.

Inside the front entrance was a scooped-out shelf. Here Little Owl sat for a while to recover from her fright. Every so often, she popped her head out to see what her neighbors were doing. But whenever she looked outside, the prairie dogs scolded her.

In time, the town quieted and the prairie dogs went their ways, nibbling and chittering.

Little Owl soon learned that a prairie dog was a good architect. He built a very snug dwelling place. In the middle of a mound of earth, almost five feet wide and a foot high, was the front entrance. This mound kept the burrow from being flooded. Even during the worst storm, the house was dry and safe.

Next to the front entrance was a housemarker. A tall weed or a thistle or a tuft of grass was always left standing to show that someone lived there.

Except for the doorsign, the front yard was kept clear of weeds and grasses. No enemy—bobcat, weasel or coyote—could creep up unseen.

As Little Owl went further down the steep tunnel, she found several chambers connected by small passageways. There was one for storing food, one for eating, and another for sleeping. This was a very fine house indeed, and here Little Owl would stay.

That afternoon, as the sun slid below the hill, she hopped out of her new home. As was her custom, she bowed a polite good evening to her neighbor.

But her neighbor was the prairie dog whose burrow she had mistakenly invaded. He began to scold her, his tail jerking angrily.

Little Owl scuttled back inside the hole.

When it was night, and the prairie dogs were sleeping, she came outside.

Quickly, she flew away to hunt. She looked for insects to eat— beetles and crickets, grasshoppers and locusts, or almost anything she could catch. Sometimes she ate small snakes, lizards, and wild mice.

A pale spring moon rose, turning the land into soft shades of light and shadow. From a distant hill, a coyote pointed his nose at the moon and sang his wild song.

As Little Owl flew through the still night, her soft-feathered wings made not even a whisper of sound. Only her shadow skimming over the ground below told of her flight.

At dawn she returned to the town and dropped beside the tall thistle weed next to her doorway. A prairie-dog sentinel alerted the community to her arrival. She quickly disappeared into her tunnel.

The next afternoon Little Owl came out to sit in the sun. At once her neighbor began to bark. And soon the whole town was barking. The noise drove Little Owl back inside.

The next day she tried again.

Gradually she came to sense that the prairie dogs would not harm her as long as she was not a threat to their homes or young. She became less frightened.

The prairie dogs did not scold as often as before, except for her neighbor. He always barked at Little Owl.

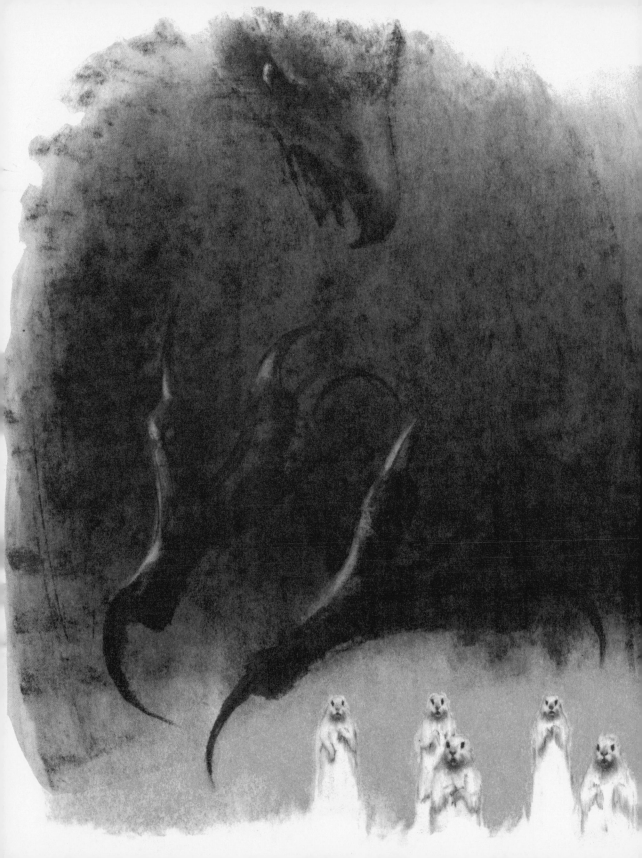

One afternoon she saw a tiny speck high in the sky. She watched. The circling shadow glided lower. It was a hawk, a dangerous enemy of the prairie dog. But no warning whistle sounded—the sentinel's eyes were not as keen as Little Owl's.

The hawk plummeted toward the ground. Down, down he dived.

Little Owl knew the danger. She cried a warning.

"Cack! Cack!"

A sentinel heard her cry and alerted the town.

Little Owl's keen eyes often saved a prairie dog from the sharp talons of a hungry eagle or hawk.

One night, during her hunt, Little Owl lit in a clump of low willows. She perched on a branch and hooted softly.

She heard an answering *Whooo—Whooo!*

A small owl flew out of the dark and settled beside her. Cooing, he gently nudged her with his beak. Later they hunted together, sharing the food they found. At dawn they flew back to the town.

Little Owl had taken a mate. They would stay together all their lives.

At first the town did not like having another owl living in their midst. The prairie dogs barked at them as the owls gathered fresh grass to line the nest they soon were building in their burrow.

When the owls came too near a prairie-dog mound, with tiny, newborn babies below, the mother, a bundle of brown fury, quickly chased them away.

Gradually the prairie dogs learned to tolerate the small owls who had come to live in their town.

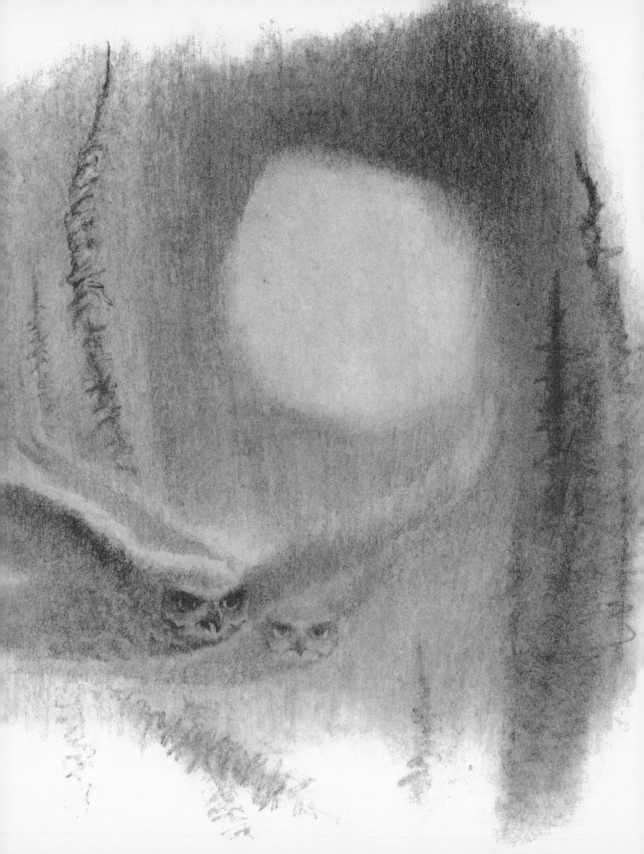

Deep underground in Little Owl's nest lay five white eggs. To keep them warm, Little Owl and her mate took turns sitting on the eggs.

One day, as Little Owl stood on her mound enjoying the warmth of the sun on her feathers, a young skunk waddled near. After a night of egg-raiding on blackbird and meadowlark nests, his stomach was full and now all he wanted was a place to curl up and take a nap. Any hole or hollow log or old stump would do.

Slowly he ambled toward Little Owl. She crouched low, clacking her beak warningly. She spread her wings and fluffed out her feathers.

Most animals would not challenge a skunk, but Little Owl would defend her nest against any enemy.

The skunk stood still. He seemed to sense her determination, or maybe he knew the danger in those sharp claws and beak. He turned away. He was much too full and sleepy to stay and contest the matter.

The prairie dog next door came out of his hole and barked at the skunk's retreating figure.

This morning Little Owl's neighbor seemed even more excited than usual. He kept running around his mound and jumping in and out of his doorway. He tried to chase Little Owl into her hole.

Nearby lived his mate and family. Underground, four baby prairie dogs lay, snuggled together. And today, for the first time, the mother was bringing the youngsters out of their burrow.

The morning sun was high when first a whisker, and then a tiny eye appeared above the hole. One by one, the little family pushed outside, until, at last, all were huddled near their mother on the mound.

Four shy, tiny prairie dogs blinked their eyes and looked around at the bright outside world. Their noses twitched with excitement, and they made soft, chirring sounds.

The father examined each of his new offspring and then sang his odd little song, telling of his joy.

When prairie dogs first mate, they live together for a few days, but they prefer to live alone. The babies stay with their mother only until they are old enough to have burrows of their own.

The mother prairie dog gathered wisps of wild grass, which she brought for her babies to eat while the father stood guard.

It was the middle of May, and Little Owl and her mate had been sitting on their eggs for over three weeks. Deep underground, in the nest of soft grasses, owlets were hatching out of their shells.

Five white, downy little owls with big, round eyes soon lay in their nest. They were very weak. It would be some time before the tiny owls would be strong enough to venture outside.

The parents were kept busy finding food for the always-open mouths of the hungry chicks.

Day by day, the owlets grew bigger and stronger. Before long, soft feathers began to replace the fluffy white down on their bodies. Now they moved about their burrow, jostling each other as they poked into every nook and corner.

The dark sky was growing lighter as, early one morning, Little Owl flew swiftly home from her hunt.

A meadowlark's happy song greeted the day. A prairie chicken moved out of a thicket, her covey of chicks following behind her.

Little Owl flew over the small hill and past the clump of sagebrush. Below was the town and home.

She saw a dark shadow slither through the grasses. She heard a hiss and then a rattle! It was the town's most dangerous enemy—a rattlesnake.

Little Owl circled above the snake. She clacked her beak threateningly. The noise alerted a prairie-dog sentinel. He stood on his hind legs and whistled a warning.

DANGER! AWAKE! DANGER!

Little Owl dived at the snake, furiously clacking her beak. The rattlesnake's head darted sideways. Slowly he slithered down into her neighbor's house.

Another sentinel warned: DANGER! DANGER!

Little Owl's neighbor scurried out the back exit of his tunnel. Several prairie dogs rushed to the front entrance and began to kick dirt and rocks down into the hole. They were trying to bury the rattlesnake, but he soon came wriggling out the backdoor.

He hissed angrily. His tail rattled a warning as he glided away through the grasses.

Little Owl quickly returned to her burrow. Everything was all right—her babies were safe.

It was time for the owlets to see the world outside. Up they struggled. Up the plunge hole.

At last they stood together on the mound, blinking their round eyes in the sunlight. Instead of scolding as he always had done before, today, the prairie dog on the next mound chittered at the owls—almost as though he were greeting the new family. The owls heard barking, as busy little prairie dogs scrambled everywhere.

Some were repairing their mounds, pushing loose earth to build them higher and stronger. Some nibbled grasses. Some sat on top of their mounds, chattering and barking to each other.

Here, in this noisy, cheerful prairie dog town, Little Owl had found a good home.

She bowed politely to her neighbors.